Farmer Tim Stories are based around experiences and situations encountered by Tim Lerwill whilst growing up on a farm in North Devon.

First Edition 2009

Published in Great Britain by Lerwill Publishing www.lerwill.co.uk

Printed and bound by Mixam UK Limited

ISBN: 978-0-9562565-0-8

The Snow Sheep

This is Puddle Farm. Tim lives here with his mum, his dad, and his big sister, Alice, who often looks after him.

Tim helps his mum and dad with everything on the farm and so they call him Farmer Tim. Being helpful leads to many wonderful adventures with his family.

One snowy night Tim lay in bed with the wind howling outside.

Whooooooooooooo

He got up and looked out of the window. All he could see was white, and cold air seeped through the window. He was always excited when it snowed and he couldn't wait for morning.

It was warm in the farmhouse and Tim went back to bed and had a little sleep.

In the morning, Tim rushed downstairs for breakfast. He had his favourite food, which was cheesy toast with lots of ketchup. Yum, yum!

Tim's dad came in through the door and he was all white. He was covered in snow from head to toe.

"It's been snowing all night long, Tim. Can you help me?" he asked. "Yes, of course I can. What is the matter, Dad?" said Tim.

"There has been an unexpected snowstorm. The sheep in the top field may be covered in snow and getting cold," said his dad. "We need to find them quickly and take them into the warm barn."

Oh dear, Tim thought as he rushed to his bedroom. He got out of his pyjamas and into his farming clothes.

"Wrap up warm," his mum shouted up the stairs. It was cold outside and the snow and ice made everything look sparkly and beautiful.

Tim asked his dad if the other farm animals were OK and he said, "Yes, they are warm and safe in the barn."

Tim and his dad got into the big red tractor and they drove up the lane to the top field.

The tractor tyres slipped and the engine chugged and roared up the steep hill. It was slow going.

There were large snowdrifts everywhere.

Tim jumped off the tractor and sank into the snow up to his knees. His welly boots filled with snow.

Dad asked Tim to carefully open the gate to the top field as he drove the tractor inside.

"Wow, that's amazing," said Tim. The top field was covered in a soft white blanket of snow and there were no sheep in sight.

Dad pulled two long sticks out from the trailer and gave one to Tim. They walked around the top field to find the sheep.

"Look!" Tim shouted. "There are sheep huddled under the hedge. They are looking very sorry for themselves."

Luckily, the sheep had thick woolly coats on which helped to keep them a bit warm.

Tim and his dad walked up behind the sheep and guided them by whistling and clapping hands. The sheep walked beside the hedge where there was less snow and into the big barn in the top field.

It was warmer inside the barn and there was hay and water for the sheep. On the floor was a bed of straw.

"Can you count the sheep for me?" Tim's dad asked. "There should be ten." Tim started,

"One, two, three, four, five,

six, seven, eight, nine, ..."

"There are only NINE, Dad!"

Tim and his dad rushed out of the barn with the sticks. "What are the sticks for?" Tim asked.

"I'll show you," Dad said.

Dad went up to a big snowdrift and carefully used his stick to prod the snow, looking for the last sheep. Tim used his stick, doing the same as his dad. Tim was pleased he was helping with an important task.

"Dad, I think I've found something!"

Tim and his dad used their hands to move the snow away. As they dug down, they carefully revealed the last and tenth sheep. She looked sleepy and walked around slowly.

They took the sheep to the barn and she soon got better and was running around with the rest of them. Her eyes looked brighter and Tim was sure she was smiling at him.

"Well done! You have helped save a sheep's life and you have been a great little farmer, Tim," said Tim's dad as they set off for home in the red tractor. Tim was happy that all the sheep were safe.

Farmer Tim stories are available from and can be ordered direct from the publisher at a price of £4.99.

Prices and availability are subject to change.

Visit our internet site www.lerwill.co.uk or email sales@lerwill.co.uk for details.